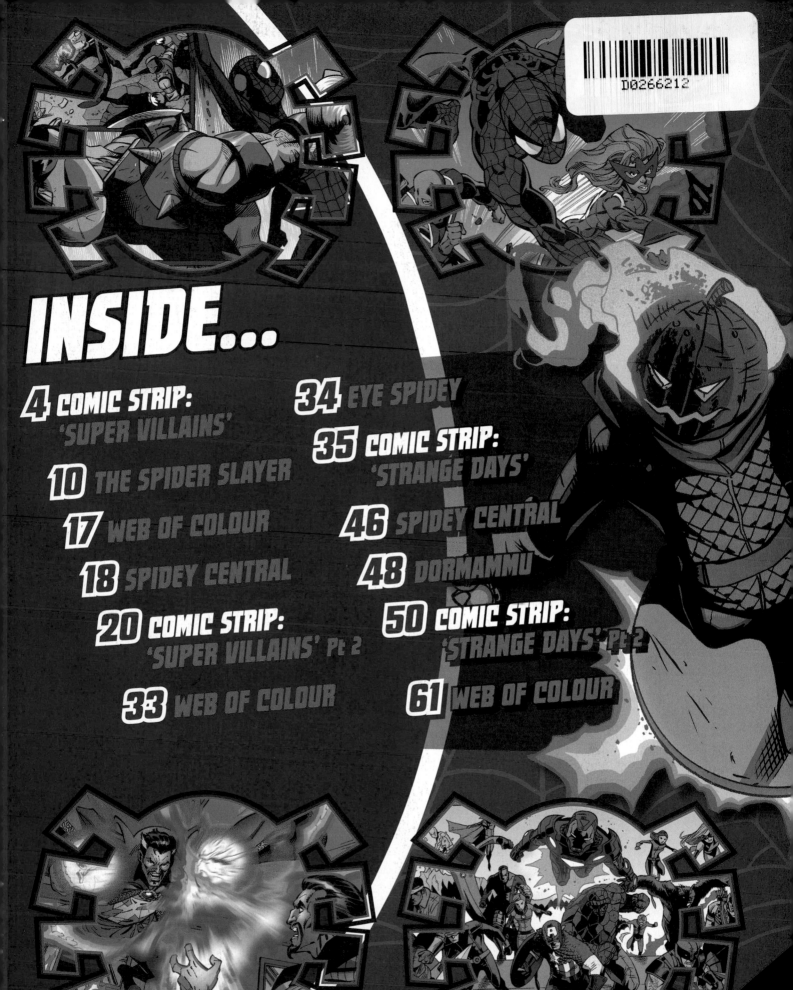

INSIDE...

D0266212

£7.99

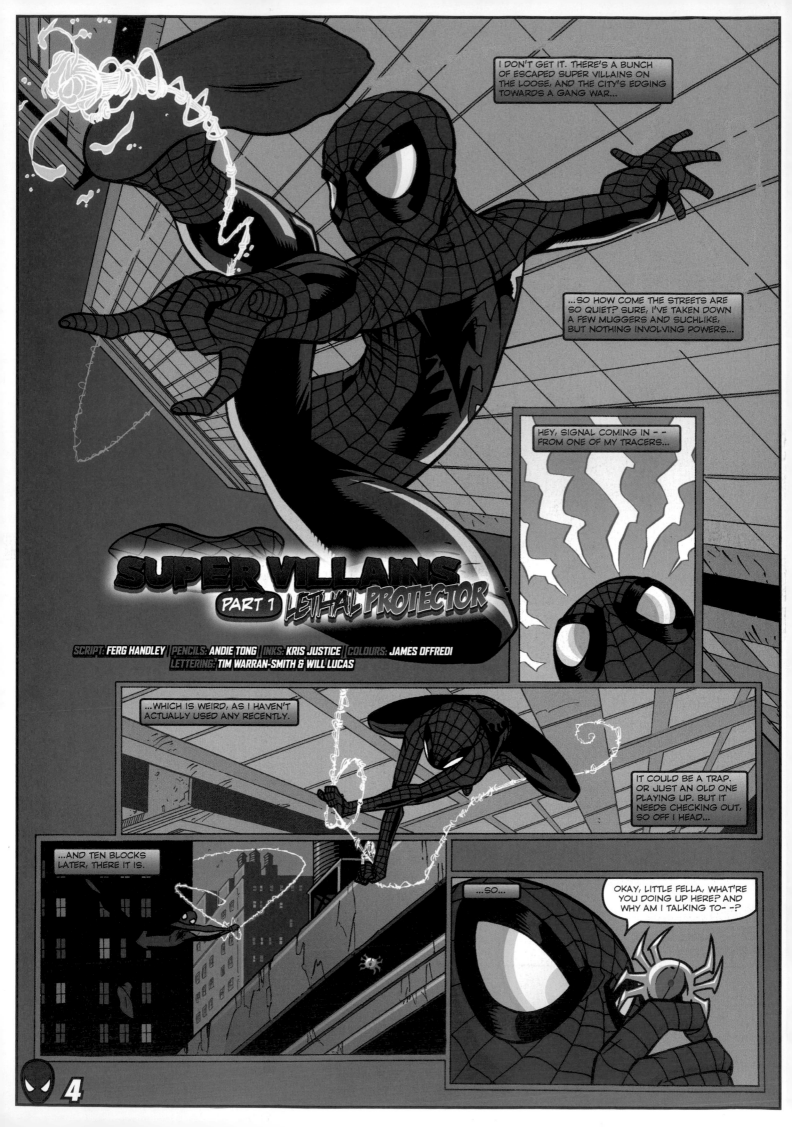

...NNN...

GOOD, YOU'RE FINALLY AWAKE.

SMYTHE! SO WHAT'S GOING ON... WHAT IS THIS PLACE?

AN OLD, ABANDONED *A.I.M.* BASE, IN UPSTATE NEW YORK. AND IT'S SWARMING WITH ENEMIES, ALL OUT TO KILL YOU.

HUH? HOW COME YOU DIDN'T JUST OFF ME WITH THE SLAYER?

*ADVANCED IDEA MECHANICS, A GLOBAL TERRORIST ORGANISATION.

OH, I WOULD HAVE...BUT MY EMPLOYER HAD OTHER PLANS.

WHAT EMPLOYER? WHO ARE YOU WORKING FOR?

I AM NOT AT LIBERTY TO DISCLOSE THAT, SPIDER-MAN.

HOWEVER, I CAN GUARANTEE THAT YOU WILL NEVER LEAVE HERE ALIVE!

WRONG, SMYTHE. AND I'LL PROVE IT, YOU'LL SEE.

WITHOUT YOUR FULL POWERS? BECAUSE THAT TRACER HAD BEEN MODIFIED, TO BLOCK YOUR SPIDER-SENSE WITH A SUBLIMINAL SIGNAL...

CONTINUED ON PAGE 12

BUILT WITH ONE PURPOSE IN MIND, AND ARMED TO THE TEETH WITH WEAPONS, THE SPIDER SLAYER DOES EXACTLY WHAT IT SAYS ON THE TIN!

TECHNO-PHOBIA

Believing Spider-Man to be a menace, Professor Spencer Smythe created a robot to fight and capture the webslinger.

FAMILY BUSINESS

But when Spidey defeated the first Slayer, Smythe became pretty miffed! He began making more and more dangerous robots, until he died of radioactive poisoning, and his son, Alistair took over.

TECHNO-PHOBIA

Alistair began building the most sophisticated Spider Slayers ever, full of claws, fangs and poisonous tails, to continue his father's Spidey-smashing legacy!

SPIDER

...AND WITHOUT IT, HE'S JUST ANOTHER Z-LIST BALD GUY!

KRUNCH

UFF!

FLAMIN' YANK -- I'LL KNOCK YER RUDDY *BILLABONG* OFF!

SURE YOU WILL, SPORT...

FWAAK

UNFF!

...AND MY NAME'S 'WALTZING MATILDA'!

SPIDER-MAN, PLEASE! IT'S *FISK'S* DOING, HONEST!

FISK? AS IN THE *KINGPIN*?

"YES, HE INVITED ME HERE, WITH MY CREW. DITTO THE OTHER BOSSES.

"AND WHOEVER SNUFFS YOU GETS TO RUN HIS ORGANISATION FOR HIM, UNTIL HE'S OUT OF JAIL."

YEAH, RIGHT. THE KINGPIN'S HARDLY THE POWER-SHARING TYPE.

IT'S *TRUE!*

HE THINKS IT'LL PREVENT A GANG WAR, WHICH WOULD BE BAD FOR ALL OUR OPERATIONS...HIS INCLUDED!

CODE BREAKER!
SPIDEY

The Spider Slayer may be asleep, but it's sending a signal to someone!

Can you use the code to work out the message it's sending?

A	B	C	D	E	F	G	H	I	J	K	L	M	N	O	P	Q	R	S	T	U	V	W	X	Y	Z

GREAT ESCAPE!

Woah, something's woken the Spider Slayer up!

Can you help Spidey outrun it by tracing a route from start to finish?

START

FINISH

SOLUTION

CENTRAL!

SHUT DOWN!

REBOOT

POWER BOOST

SHUT DOWN

DEPLOY WEAPONS

ABCD

Looks like Spidey's gonna have to take care of the Spider Slayer after all!

Follow the wires to choose the correct button to shut it down!

ANSWER

ANIMAL-ALIAS!

Owl and Kangaroo aren't the only Super Villains named after animals!

Draw lines to match these villains to their animal counterparts!

1.

2.

3.

4.

A

B

C

D

IF THERE WAS A TOWN CALLED SUCKVILLE, THEY'D PROBABLY MAKE ME MAYOR.

LIKE, IN ONE NIGHT, I'VE BEEN ZAPPED, GASSED, KIDNAPPED, DEPRIVED OF MY SPIDER-SENSE AND AMBUSHED BY GANGS OF SUPER VILLAINS...

...AND NOW I'VE GOT VENOM BEARING DOWN ON ME. I MEAN VENOM, FOR CRYING OUT LOUD!

SUPER VILLAINS
PART 2 LETHAL PROTECTOR

SCRIPT: **FERG HANDLEY** PENCILS: **ANDIE TONG** INKS: **KRIS JUSTICE**
COLOURS: **JAMES OFFREDI** LETTERING: **WILL LUCAS**

STILL, NO WAY I'M GOING DOWN WITHOUT A FIGHT...

WAIT! WE'RE ON YOUR SIDE, SPIDER-MAN!

ALRIGHT, TOOTHY. I DON'T CARE WHICH WISE GUY YOU'RE WORKING FOR- -

IT'S QUITE SIMPLE. YES, WE WERE RECRUITED BY HAMMERHEAD...

...BUT WHEN WE LEARNED ABOUT THE KINGPIN'S PLAN, WE QUIT!

WHOA! YOU'RE WHAT?

WEB OF COLOUR!

HEY SPIDER-FANS! TIME TO GRAB THOSE PENS AND GET COLOURING. DON'T GO OVER THOSE LINES NOW!

EYE SPIDEY!

CAN YOU SPOT 10 DIFFERENCES BETWEEN THESE TWO PICTURES?

HAPPY HOLIDAYS, SPIDER-FREAK! I HOPE YOU ENJOY THE PRESENT THAT I'VE SENT YOU!

WHAT, YOU MEAN THE SCARY TEAM OF NINJAS? YOU KNOW AUNT MAY GOT ME THE SAME THING LAST YEAR, RIGHT?

ANSWERS: Colour of ninja in top left; snowman in background; missing ninja star to Spidey's right; missing ninja star to Spidey's left; baseball bat; missing ninja in bottom right; Spidey's mug; missing crossbow; window in bottom left; skyscraper lights in bottom right.

34

...AND A FEW MINUTES LATER, THE DOC'S BACK ON HIS FEET.

SO WHAT GIVES, STEVE-O? LIKE, I KNOW MORDO'S TROUBLE, BUT YOU'VE NORMALLY GOT IT COVERED.

I AM ALSO PUZZLED, SPIDER-MAN.

ALL I KNOW IS THAT HE SUDDENLY APPEARED, MORE POWERFUL THAN EVER, AND LAUNCHED AN OVERWHELMING ATTACK.

STILL, IT COULD BE WORSE. I MEAN, ALL HE TOOK WAS SOME CRYSTAL-LOOKING THINGAMAJIG.

CRYSTAL...?

OSHTUR PRESERVE US! THE OBJECT YOU REFER TO IS THE STONE OF BELANOS... AN ANCIENT AND DANGEROUS ARTEFACT ONCE ENTRUSTED INTO MY CARE.

EM, NOT LIKING THE SOUND OF THIS, DOC.

"WITH GOOD REASON, SPIDER-MAN. THE STONE IS A TYPE OF MYSTICAL KEY, CAPABLE OF OPENING A PORTAL TO THE DARK DIMENSION..."

"...A FOUL, MONSTROUS REALM, INHABITED BY DEMONS AND RULED BY MY GREATEST FOE -- THE DREAD DORMAMMU!"

NOW, DORMAMMU WAS ONCE FORCED TO SWEAR AN OATH, WHICH FORBIDS HIM TO ENTER EARTH'S PLANE.

HOWEVER, HE CAN USE AGENTS TO FURTHER HIS DESIGNS... WHICH WOULD EXPLAIN MORDO'S HEIGHTENED POWERS.

37